The Mystery of Redemption
and Christian Discipleship

Student Workbook

The Didache Series

– SEMESTER EDITION –

The Mystery of Redemption
and Christian Discipleship

Student Workbook

Midwest Theological Forum

Downers Grove, Illinois

Published in the United States of America by

Midwest Theological Forum
4340 Cross Street, Suite 1
Downers Grove, Illinois 60515 USA
(630) 541-8519
www.theologicalforum.org

Publisher:	Rev. James Socias
Editor-in-Chief:	Jeffrey Cole
Editorial Board:	Rev. James Socias, Rev. Peter Armenio, Scott Hahn, Ph.D., Jeffrey Cole
Other Contributors:	Kevin Aldrich, Matthew A. Rarey
Layout Design and Production:	Stephen J. Chojnicki

Disclaimer: The editor of this book has attempted to give proper credit to all sources used in the text and illustrations. Any miscredit or lack of credit is unintended and will be corrected in the next edition.

ISBN 978-1-939231-07-9

Contents

Abbreviations Used for the Books of the Bible   vi

Chapter 1: In the Beginning   1

Chapter 2: Preparing for the Messiah   19

Chapter 3: The Promise of Redemption Is Fulfilled in Christ   37

Chapter 4: The Light of the World: Redemption Revealed   59

Chapter 5: Redemption Through the Paschal Mystery   77

Chapter 6: Our Response to the Gift of Redemption   93

Chapter 7: Prayer in the Life of a Believer   121

Appendix: Challenges to Faith in the Redemption   143

Catholic Prayers and Devotions   151

Abbreviations Used for the Books of the Bible

Gn	Genesis	Sir	Sirach	Acts	Acts of the Apostles
Ex	Exodus	Is	Isaiah	Rom	Romans
Lv	Leviticus	Jer	Jeremiah	1 Cor	1 Corinthians
Nm	Numbers	Lam	Lamentations	2 Cor	2 Corinthians
Dt	Deuteronomy	Bar	Baruch	Gal	Galatians
Jos	Joshua	Ez	Ezekiel	Eph	Ephesians
Jgs	Judges	Dn	Daniel	Phil	Philippians
Ru	Ruth	Hos	Hosea	Col	Colossians
1 Sm	1 Samuel	Jl	Joel	1 Thes	1 Thessalonians
2 Sm	2 Samuel	Am	Amos	2 Thes	2 Thessalonians
1 Kgs	1 Kings	Ob	Obadiah	1 Tm	1 Timothy
2 Kgs	2 Kings	Jon	Jonah	2 Tm	2 Timothy
1 Chr	1 Chronicles	Mi	Micah	Ti	Titus
2 Chr	2 Chronicles	Na	Nahum	Phlm	Philemon
Ezr	Ezra	Hb	Habakkuk	Heb	Hebrews
Neh	Nehemiah	Zep	Zephaniah	Jas	James
Tb	Tobit	Hg	Haggai	1 Pt	1 Peter
Jdt	Judith	Zec	Zechariah	2 Pt	2 Peter
Est	Esther	Mal	Malachi	1 Jn	1 John
Jb	Job	1 Mc	1 Maccabees	2 Jn	2 John
Ps	Psalms	2 Mc	2 Maccabees	3 Jn	3 John
Prv	Proverbs	Mt	Matthew	Jude	Jude
Eccl	Ecclesiastes	Mk	Mark	Rev	Revelation
Sg	Song of Songs	Lk	Luke		
Wis	Wisdom	Jn	John		

textbook
p. 1

Chapter 1

IN THE BEGINNING

INTRODUCTION

1. What do the opening chapters of Genesis reveal about God's special relationship with human beings?

2. What does the creation narrative reveal about the human being's place within creation?

3. What was Adam and Eve's original condition?

4. What disrupted the original harmony of Paradise?

5. What did Original Sin do to the world?

6. How did God respond to the disobedience of Adam and Eve?

WHAT CATHOLICS BELIEVE ABOUT THE BIBLE

7. According to the *Catechism*, no. 141, what do Sacred Scripture and the Eucharist have in common for faithful believers?

8. How many books are in the Bible?

9. How is salvation history different from other kinds of history?

10. How was the Bible divinely inspired?

11. What is the relationship between the Holy Spirit and the human writers of Scripture?

12. Why is it impossible for the Bible to be in error?

THE BIBLE IS SACRED LITERATURE

13. Why is the Bible *sacred* literature?

14. What are some of the various genres in which Sacred Scripture is written?

15. How old is the Bible?

THE BIBLE REVEALS HISTORY FROM GOD'S POINT OF VIEW

16. What is the root meaning of the word "religion"?

17. How did ancient peoples view religion?

18. Despite modern peoples pretending to write objective history, how are all of our histories actually quite subjective?

19. To the sacred authors, what was the most important thing about history?

THE LITERAL AND SPIRITUAL SENSES OF THE BIBLE

20. How can we understand the *literal* sense of a passage of Scripture?

21. Give an example of a false literalistic interpretation of the Bible.

22. Why can there be no contradiction between the literal and spiritual senses of the Bible?

23. What is an example of the *allegorical*, or *typical*, sense of Sacred Scripture?

24. What is an example of the *moral*, or *tropological*, sense of Sacred Scripture?

SIDEBAR: HOW THE BIBLE WAS WRITTEN

25. Why do some of the passages in the Bible that mention physical or astronomical phenomena seem outdated to us?

26. What institution gives us the ability to understand difficult passages in the Bible?

27. *Critical Thinking*: What might happen if a person were to read the Bible, come across passages that were not immediately clear, and have no definitive authority to which he or she can appeal in order to interpret and to understand it correctly? Does it even make a difference how a person interprets the Bible?

RELIGIOUS TRUTH, NOT SCIENTIFIC TRUTH

28. What is the error of scientific creationism?

29. What error is the opposite of creationism?

30. What is the "both/and" approach to interpreting the creation narrative in Genesis?

31. How can faith elevate reason?

32. Why can faith and reason not be in real conflict?

33. How has the religious message of the Bible helped Western civilization give birth to and advance modern science?

GOD CREATED THE WORLD

34. What does the word *genesis* mean?

35. What doctrine does the sacred author of Genesis teach by writing, "God created the heavens and the earth"?

36. What is the significance of the six-day creation narrative?

37. Does the Catholic faith understand Genesis to mean that human beings are free to do whatever they want in or to the world?

38. Have human beings obeyed God's command to "subdue" the earth?

SIDEBAR: IS IT TRUE?

39. What question is being asked in the sidebar, "Is It True"?

40. What answer does the text of the sidebar give to your answer to the previous question?

CREATION AS THE WORK OF THE BLESSED TRINITY

41. To what extent can we understand the nature of the Blessed Trinity?

42. Why is assigning specific roles to each of the Persons of the Blessed Trinity erroneous?

43. Who is the Word of God that was "spoken" by the Father in each command in the creation narrative?

44. What is the "Spirit of God" and the "breath of life" mentioned in the creation narrative?

45. How did the early Christians view the use of the plural pronouns in the creation narrative?

SIDEBAR: CREATION AND EVOLUTION

46. Give an example of a truth found in Genesis that the Church requires Christians to accept.

47. What does the Church teach in general about the various scientific theories of evolution?

48. *Critical Thinking*: In light of the Catholic faith, how would you answer someone who claimed that both human beings and apes descended from a common ancestor?

IMAGE AND LIKENESS

49. Among all creatures in visible creation, why are human beings uniquely privileged?

50. What is the source of every human being's body and soul?

51. What is the relationship between body and soul?

GOD MADE THEM MALE AND FEMALE

52. What does it mean to say that men and women are *different* but *complementary*?

53. In relation to each other, in what state of life were Adam and Eve created?

54. Why did Christ quote Genesis: "For this reason a man shall leave his father and mother and be joined to his wife, and the two shall become one flesh" (Mt 19:5)?

55. What is marriage?

56. How does human sexuality relate to fruitfulness in marriage?

57. How is marriage good for society?

SIDEBAR: CHARITY AND CHASTITY

58. What does the practice of chastity mean for single people?

59. What does the practice of chastity mean for married people?

60. *Critical Thinking*: How is exercising chastity a charitable act?

THE ORIGINAL STATE OF MAN

61. What preternatural gifts did our first parents possess?

62. What supernatural gifts did our first parents possess?

63. What work were our first parents given to do?

THE CREATION OF ANGELS

64. What is the only example of a material and spiritual creature?

65. In what ways do angels cooperate in God's plan of salvation for all people?

66. What is a guardian angel?

SATAN AND THE FALLEN ANGELS

67. Who is Satan, or the Devil, and what mission do he and his followers pursue?

68. Why does God allow demons to test people?

69. How powerful is Satan?

ORIGINAL SIN

70. How was Original Sin a sin of disobedience?

71. According to the *Catechism*, no. 398, how was Original Sin a rejection of God?

72. *Critical Thinking*: If a person does not acknowledge his or her limits as a creature and submit his or her behavior to God's will, what is possible?

THE CONSEQUENCES OF ORIGINAL SIN

73. In terms of how people relate to one another, what is one consequence of Original Sin?

ORIGINAL SIN AFFECTS ALL OF HUMANITY

74. Did Original Sin destroy human nature?

75. How are the effects of the fall manifested in Adam and Eve's immediate descendants?

76. What is the relationship between Original Sin and every person's actual sins?

SIDEBAR: ST. ELIZABETH ANN SETON

77. What does it mean to say that St. Elizabeth Ann Seton understood both lay and religious life?

78. Why is St. Elizabeth important to the Catholic Church in the United States of America?

79. What trials did St. Elizabeth suffer, and how did she endure them?

SIN AND OUR NEED FOR REDEMPTION

80. How did God respond to the fall of Adam and Eve?

81. What would be the culmination of God's plan of redemption?

82. According to St. Paul, how is Christ a "New Adam" (Rom 5:19)?

SUPPLEMENTARY READING

83. According to St. Peter Chrysologus, what qualities of Christ should Christians imitate to be like God, and what quality should they not imitate?

20. How was Noah different from his contemporaries?

21. What does the number *forty* symbolize in the Bible? Give examples.

22. What did the *forty days* represent in the case of the flood?

23. How did the descendants of Noah divide between good and evil?

24. Of what is the Tower of Babel a symbol?

25. How does Christ overcome the sin at the Tower of Babel definitively, and how did the Holy Spirit do this at Pentecost specifically?

26. What is the Paschal Mystery, and how does it relate to God's original plan for human beings?

THE COVENANTS PREPARE GOD'S PEOPLE FOR REDEMPTION

27. What happened to the Old Testament covenants in general as time progressed? Give illustrative examples.

28. *Critical Thinking*: God's covenants were broken repeatedly by his people. Why do you think God kept offering them more and more chances to be faithful?

GOD'S COVENANT WITH NOAH

29. Of what are the "clean animals," which Noah sacrificed after the flood, a type?

30. What foods does God allow human beings to eat in the covenant with Noah?

31. How were the cleansing effects of the flood only temporary, and how did they become permanent?

SIDEBAR: HOW THE OLD TESTAMENT COVENANTS FORESHADOW THE REDEMPTION

32. According to the *Catechism*, no. 129, how should the Old and New Testaments be read, and thus what "old saying" does the *Catechism* affirm?

33. How did St. Peter describe Noah and the flood's symbolic relation to Baptism?

34. According to the *Catechism*, no. 527, what does circumcision, which is the sign of the covenant with Abraham, prefigure, and how does that relate to the redemption?

35. How does the Exodus narrative foreshadow Christ's redemption?

36. How is the passage of the Israelites through the Red Sea a type of the Sacrament of Baptism?

GOD'S COVENANT WITH ABRAHAM

37. What did God initiate in his covenant with Abraham?

38. *Critical Thinking*: Explain how Abraham can be considered a model for your life of faith.

39. *Critical Thinking*: How did Abraham's willingness to sacrifice Isaac prefigure the Sacrifice of Christ on the Cross?

GOD'S COVENANT WITH MOSES

40. What purpose did the Mosaic Law serve in regard to the chosen people and the coming of the Messiah, and, in turn, what did the Messiah do in terms of the Mosaic Law?

41. Who were the Israelites, who was Joseph, and why did the Israelites move from the promised land to Egypt?

42. What did Christ say that echoed the divine name, "I AM WHO I AM"?

43. According to the *Catechism*, no. 62, why did God, through Moses, give the Israelites his law?

44. What is the content of the Ten Commandments?

45. What did God make clear about what fidelity or disobedience to the Ten Commandments would entail?

46. Even though the Ten Commandments are part of the natural law, which is binding on everyone and discoverable through human reason, why did God reveal them explicitly to the chosen people?

47. *Critical Thinking*: Read an account of a Jewish Seder Meal, commemorating the original Passover, and then list thee ways this ritual resonates with the Mass.

ENTRUSTED WITH GOD'S PROMISES

48. How did the chosen people acquire the promised land?

49. Who were the judges, and what role did they serve?

50. Were the judges successful ultimately in keeping Israel in line?

51. In response to Israel's anarchy, for what did the people beseech God?

52. Who was Israel's first king?

53. What did God instruct Samuel to do in light of Saul's unworthiness?

SIDEBAR: ST. TERESA BENEDICTA OF THE CROSS

54. Whose writings led to Edith Stein's conversion from atheism?

55. What was St. Teresa Benedicta's idea of the "natural vocation of women" in society?

56. Although it is not clear that St. Teresa's petition for the Pope to denounce Nazism was directly responsible, what did Pope Pius XI do in 1937 that angered the Nazi regime?

57. What did St. Teresa's Carmelite Order do to try to help her avoid the Nazi threat?

58. Sensing the Nazi threat, for what did St. Teresa offer her life?

59. *Critical Thinking*: Write a paragraph addressing the aspects of St. Teresa's life—her character, her intellectual honesty, her faith, her courage, etc.—that you find to be most striking and why.

THE PROMISE TO DAVID

60. Of the many Old Testament figures, who serves particularly as a type of Christ?

61. What happened to Israel after Saul had died and David had become king?

62. What did David do for Jerusalem?

63. How is Jersusalem associated with Abraham, Solomon, and Christ?

64. How did the idea of divine sonship change with David?

65. *Critical Thinking*: As punishment for David's sin, God offered him three choices for his people: a famine, defeat in war, or a plague. Study the painting *King David in Prayer* (p. 50) and read 2 Samuel 24:10–15. What elements did the painter Grebber use to depict each of these three choices?

PROMISES MADE THROUGH THE PROPHETS

66. What did the prophets warn if Israel would turn against God?

67. Who conquered the Northern Kingdom of Israel?

68. As Israel experienced chaos and collapse following the reign of Solomon, what did the prophets promise?

69. According to the *Catechism*, no. 436, how did the title *Messiah* become proper to Jesus, who is called *Jesus Christ*, or simply *Christ*?

70. Again according to the *Catechism*, no. 436, what threefold anointing did Jesus receive as Messiah?

71. What did the prophet Isaiah state clearly about the coming savior?

72. According to the prophet Isaiah, how would this savior achieve his final victory?

73. How did Christ fulfill Isaiah's prophecy of the Suffering Servant?

74. What type of suffering did Christ undergo perhaps most of all, and why?

75. What was the immediate reason for Christ's supreme Sacrifice?

76. How can our personal suffering serve as a conduit to Christ, the Suffering Servant?

77. What happened to Judah about 150 years after the time of the prophet Isaiah?

SIDEBAR: CHRIST, THE SUFFERING SERVANT

78. *Critical Thinking*: Choose five of Isaiah's predictions about the Suffering Servant from the sidebar "Christ, the Suffering Servant" (p. 53) and explain how they were fulfilled in Christ.

SUPPLEMENTARY READING

79. What is the "kindly cloud" of which St. Ambrose wrote, whom did it visit, and how is it associated with the Mother of God?

80. What prefigurement did St. Ambrose see between Moses at the spring of Marah and Christ, his Cross, and the waters of Baptism?

81. According to Pope Bl. John XXIII, what is God's precondition for revealing himself to people?

82. According to St. Irenæus, how did God treat Satan and our disobedient first parents differently, and why?

83. According to St. Irenæus, what will be the eventual outcome of the *Protoevangelium*?

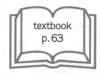
name Kathleen McVerney

Chapter 3

THE PROMISE OF REDEMPTION
IS FULFILLED IN CHRIST

INTRODUCTION

1. According to the *Catechism*, no. 422, what is the essence of "the gospel of Jesus Christ"?

    God sending his son to earth to be born by a woman

2. What act of cooperation made it possible for God the Son to enter human history?

    Mary agreeing to have Jesus.

3. When did the redemption of human beings begin to unfold finally?

    Jesus' birth

THE ANNUNCIATION

4. What kind of savior were many Israelites hoping would arrive at the time of Christ?

    A military leader

5. In what towns did the Annunciation and the Nativity occur?

Nazareth

6. What is the Paschal Mystery, and when did it begin?

the redemption of the suffering, death,
resurrection, and ascension began w/the annunciation

7. What does the phrase "the fullness of time" describe?

the moment when God's promise of a redeemer
would be revealed.

8. What was necessary for "the fullness of time" to be reached?

Mary's Cooperation

9. *Critical Thinking*: If "the fullness of time" means that the time had come when Israel was finally prepared to accept her savior, why did many of these same people reject and kill him?

Not everyone would ever be ready

10. Why did God want the Blessed Virgin Mary to play a vital role in his plan of salvation?

So she cowd serue as a model disciple

11. How did the Archangel Gabriel underline the message that the Blessed Virgin Mary's child is divine?

He wowd be the son of God

12. What does the name *Jesus* mean?

God saves

13. Why did every act of Christ on earth have a redemptive value for the salvation of human beings?

We need that much redemption

14. What necessary condition did the Blessed Virgin Mary fulfill for the redemption to take place?

Her saying yes

15. To what does the Blessed Virgin Mary's *fiat* refer?

Her saying yes to God.

16. Why is the Blessed Virgin Mary called the *New Eve?*

> Her obedience) makes up for
> Eve's disobedience

17. *Critical Thinking:* Why is the doctrine of the Virgin Birth of Christ central to Christianity?

> It's the only thing
> It shows that Jesus is divine.

SIDEBAR: "FULL OF GRACE" EXEMPTED FROM ORIGINAL SIN

18. Applied to the Blessed Virgin Mary, what does the Greek *kecharitomene*, or "full of grace," mean?

> Mary was full of God's grace (Jesus)

19. Although it has been a perennial teaching of the Church, when was the Immaculate Conception of the Blessed Virgin Mary declared a dogma of the faith, i.e., solemnly defined, and by whom?

> Pope Bl. Pius IX in 1854

20. Did the Blessed Virgin Mary ever sin?

> Nope, never

ST. JOSEPH'S DREAM

21. What does it mean when the Scriptures call St. Joseph a "just man"?

He was a holy, faithful man.

22. What was a betrothal at the time of Christ?

A promise of marriage

23. How did St. Joseph react when he learned that his betrothed, the Blessed Virgin Mary, was with child?

He didn't want to shame her, so he tried to quietly divorce her.

24. Why did St. Joseph resolve to divorce the Blessed Virgin Mary quietly?

He didn't want to shame her

25. What changed St. Joseph's mind about marrying the Blessed Virgin Mary?

An angel came to him and said the child was divine.

26. What was St. Joseph's heroic act of faith?

He married Mary

27. What part do people play in Christ's redemption?

We have to cooperate and imitate his generosity.

28. *Critical Thinking*: What was St. Joseph's vocation, and how is he a model for following your God-given vocation?

He took care of Mary and acted as Jesus' father, as we should care for others too.

"PREPARE THE WAY OF THE LORD"

29. What are three of the prophecies that were fulfilled by the Incarnation?

genealogy of christ, birth place, called the son of God.

30. When did St. John the Baptist first recognize the Christ?

When he was in Elizabeth's womb, and Christ was in Mary's.

31. How did St. John the Baptist fulfill the prophecy of Isaiah, "A voice cries: / "In the wilderness prepare the way of the Lord, / make straight in the desert a highway for our God" (Is 40:3)?

John the Baptist prepared the way for God by baptizing people.

32. How did St. John the Baptist compare his baptism to the Baptism that the Messiah would offer?

His was only w/water, not the Holy spirit and Fire.

33. Why did the sinless Christ want to be baptized by St. John?

to accept his mission by identifying himself w/sinners.

WHY THE WORD BECAME FLESH

34. What does the phrase, "the Word became flesh," mean?

God's love created a human being.

35. *Critical Thinking*: Jesus Christ is, in the words of the Nicene Creed, "true God from true God . . . and became man." How was Christ's human nature manifested during his life on earth? What lessons can be learned from his humanity?

> He felt pain and suffering, as well as sorrow. He had all the good sides of humanity, and showed us how to live.

36. What do *reconcile* and *expiation* mean?

> To reconcile is to come back from, to come back together. Expiation means not reconciling.

37. Why is Original Sin infinitely serious, and how does this relate to Christ's having to reconcile us to God?

> Original sin shows that we have the potential for evil inside us, and God needs to save us.

38. Why was a sacrifice necessary to repair the damage caused by sin?

> Our sins would have led to our death.

39. How did God reconcile the human race to himself?

He sent his only Son to save us

40. Why did God want to display his immense love for human beings?

Because he loves us a whole lot

41. How does creation itself show God's love?

We were created in his image

42. Why did God choose to suffer and to die to save human beings?

So we did not have to.

43. Why did God become incarnate?

To be closer to us

44. On what is the imitation of Christ based?

    It is based on God's image

45. What role do the Beatitudes play in learning holiness?

    We follow them to become holy.

46. How are we to engage the life and words of Christ found in the Gospels?

    Immitate him in sacrifice, and follow the Beatitudes.

47. What example of Christ's call to imitate him did he display during the Last Supper?

    He said to Love God and with all your heart, mind, and soul.

48. *Critical Thinking*: How has Christ's model of holiness inspired you to go beyond yourself to serve others in imitation of him? In one paragraph, cite a specific example from your life. If you cannot think of an example, consider a circumstance in which you could be "another Christ."

    I try to be kind to people, to put their needs up there w/ mine.

49. According to the *Catechism*, no. 460, why did the Word become flesh?

to make us partakers of the divine nature

50. What can we do to grow in the divine life?

We can cooperate in sanctifying grace
and immitate christ

51. What did Christ institute to be the primary means of receiving sanctifying as well as actual graces?

The Seven Sacraments

52. How do we receive actual graces?

God gives them to us under
special circumstances

53. What is the significance of Christ's example of the vine and the branches for living the divine life?

We come from God. We are a part of him.

54. What makes it possible for us to obey the New Commandment of love?

By christ making available abundant grace

55. Can a person become Christlike by his or her efforts alone?

No, you need God's help.

56. How did sin enter the world?

Through the works of Satan, who tempted Adam and Eve.

57. How did death enter the world?

Adam and Eve fell into temptation and were expelled from Eden.

58. How is Christ's victory over the Devil something of a work in progress?

He can't defeat the devil unless all of us resist him.

59. When will Satan be vanquished forever, and who will be vanquished along with him?

Probably not until all humans are gone. And animals. But then everyone who rejected God will be gone too.

60. *Critical Thinking*: What role did Satan play in Christ's Death? You might start by considering his role in bringing sin into the world or reading one of the Passion narratives in the Gospels.

No one would have thought to kill a person without evil in the world. The Devil represents the hatred in our heart's that lead us to awful things.

SIDEBAR: HOLINESS: MEDITATING ON THE PASSION

61. What four main things does the Passion of Christ teach us?

62. *Critical Thinking*: How can your own life experiences be an opportunity for charity?

SIDEBAR: ST. CHARLES BORROMEO

63. What was the purpose of the Ecumenical Council of Trent, whose reforms St. Charles Borromeo implemented successfully?

64. Did St. Charles have an easy time reforming the Church in Milan?

65. *Critical Thinking*: Identify three ways in which St. Charles lived a life of Christian service.

CHRIST'S ENTIRE LIFE WAS A MYSTERY OF REDEMPTION

66. What part of Christ's life was redemptive?

67. When did the intervention of Jesus Christ in the world begin?

68. What is the purpose of the mystery of the Incarnation?

69. What "instrument" did God use to redeem us, and how was this truth reflected?

70. What is Christian poverty, or detachment, and what does it involve?

71. Why do followers of Christ need to practice poverty, or detachment?

72. How does poverty, or detachment, reflect Christ's redemptive mission?

73. How does Christian poverty relate to the Beatitude about the "poor in spirit"?

74. *Critical Thinking*: What is one thing in your life to which you are unduly attached, something that makes you focused inwardly to the neglect of God and others? (If you cannot think of any such hindrance in your life, consider how you would counsel a friend who does in order to help him or her to live out a life in imitation of Christ.) How might you address this problem in order to draw closer to God and to others? Record some of your thoughts in a private location such as a notebook or diary.

75. To whom, other than his heavenly Father, was Christ obedient?

76. What did Christ spend most of his years on earth doing?

77. What does your answer to the previous question teach you regarding your own life and how you are to live every day?

78. How does obedience reflect Christ's redemptive mission?

79. How does the good news of the redemption first come to us?

80. How do Christ's words prompt an examination of conscience?

81. What is necessary on our part for the Word of God to become effective?

82. How did Christ reveal the love of the Father during his earthly ministry?

83. What is compassion?

84. How does mercy, or compassion, reflect Christ's redemptive mission?

85. Why did Christ not heal every person?

86. According to the *Catechism*, no. 549, what was the greatest form of slavery from which Christ came to free people?

87. *Critical Thinking*: When encountering a difficulty or unpleasant task, we are taught to "offer it up" to God. How does offering up to God such things unite us to Christ?

WE ARE JUSTIFIED IN CHRIST

88. According to the *Catechism*, no. 1996, what does *justification by grace* mean?

89. According to the *Catechism*, no. 1990, what does justification do for us?

90. What does redemption *take away from* and *add to* a person?

91. How can we grow in sanctifying grace?

SIDEBAR: JUSTIFIED BY FAITH AND WORKS

92. What was Martin Luther's doctrine of justification?

93. What was St. James's view of faith and works?

94. How do good works relate to justification?

95. *Critical Thinking*: The theological virtues are faith, hope, and charity. How does charity function in relation to faith and works?

CHRIST'S ENTIRE LIFE REVEALS THE FATHER

96. If we want to know what God the Father is like, where can we look?

97. Who or what is the fullness of God's self-Revelation?

98. According to St. John, who is the only person who has ever seen God the Father?

SUPPLEMENTARY READING

99. According to Pope Paul VI, what can learn from the "school" of Nazareth, especially as it shines light on who Christ is?

Chapter 4

THE LIGHT OF THE WORLD: REDEMPTION REVEALED

INTRODUCTION

1. In Sacred Scripture as a whole, what do light and darkness symbolize?

    Light symbolizes good, and darkness evil, or a lack of God.

2. According to Pope St. John Paul II, how do the Luminous Mysteries relate to Christ's redemptive mission?

    These mysteries consider the public life of Jesus Christ and the unfolding of his role in redemption.

3. How did Christ reveal the Kingdom of God during his public life?

    He proclaims the kingdom of God, and his very life reveals the kingdom.

THE BAPTISM OF CHRIST

4. What was St. John the Baptist's mission, and how did he carry it out?

    His mission was to prepare the world for Christ, which he did by baptizing for repentance.

5. When a priest or bishop who is celebrating the Mass holds up the host and says, "Behold the Lamb of God, / behold him who takes away the sins of the world," what is he calling us to recognize?

He wants us to recognize Jesus' sacrifice.

6. According to the *Catechism*, what did the baptism of Christ by St. John indicate?

It indicated that Christ is here to serve the lowly.

7. What did Christ mean when he said that he needed to be baptized "to fulfill all righteousness"?

He meant that even he was human, & he needed to be a good example.

8. What does *kenosis* mean in reference to Christ and his redemption?

Kenosis means self-emptying, as Christ sacrificed hisself.

9. How do Christians participate in the Paschal Mystery when they receive the Sacrament of Baptism?

We are freed from our sins & saved by Jesus.

10. What is symbolized more strongly when Baptism is administered by *immersion*?

We are drowning our sins and being covered in reedemption.

11. How was Christ's baptism a manifestation of the Blessed Trinity?

It was the first time all the trinity's people were present at the same time.

12. What phase in Christ's life did his baptism begin?

It began his missionary phase.

13. According to the *Catechism*, no. 538, what do Christ's temptations in the wilderness recapitulate?

It recapitulates Adam's failing to resist temptation.

14. Why is it meaningful that Christ spent *forty* days in the wilderness?

Forty indicates a period of trial in the Bible.

15. How is Christ's forty days in the wilderness a prototype of Lent?

He gave up things and suffered to become closer to God, as we should during Lent.

16. On what three levels did Satan tempt Christ?

He was tempted physically, mentally, and spiritually.

17. What did Christ reveal by rejecting Satan's temptations?

He revealed that people don't need to give in to their sinful ways.

18. According to Pope Benedict XVI, what is Christ's answer to the tempter's lies about the value of power and prosperity?

God is man's true food.

19. According to the *Catechism*, no. 539, what does Christ's defeat of Satan in the wilderness and his obedience to the Father foreshadow?

It foreshadows how he will defeat sin on the cross.

20 *Critical Thinking*: Why did Satan seize the opportunity to tempt Christ repeatedly while he fasted for forty days in the solitude of the wilderness? What does this reveal to you about Satan's tactics?

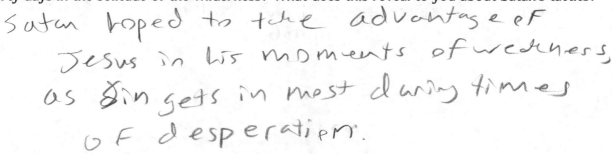

Satan hoped to tehe advantage of Jesus in his moments of weakness, as sin gets in most during times of desperation.

THE MIRACLE AT CANA

21. In what two scenes does the Blessed Virgin Mary appear in St. John's Gospel?

22. Why did the possibility of changing water into wine at Cana necessarily begin the public phase of Christ's redemptive mission?

23. *Critical Thinking*: How did the Blessed Virgin Mary act as Mother, Intercessor, and Cooperator with the redemption at the wedding feast at Cana?

24. *Critical Thinking*: Study the painting *The Wedding at Cana* (p. 98). How was Christ's role in the serving of the miraculous wine at the wedding feast at Cana a prefigurement of the distribution of Holy Communion in his Church?

THE PROCLAMATION OF THE KINGDOM

25. Who is the king in the Kingdom of God?

God is King.

26. How can the Kingdom of God be both "at hand" and "not of this world"?

It is greater than this world, but a part of it

27. What is the visible sign of the Kingdom of God on earth?

Jesus Christ is the visible sign.

28. According to the *Catechism*, no. 542, what established the Kingdom of God definitively?

Jesus' death on the cross.

29. What does it mean for us that the Kingdom of God is missionary?

It travels and reaches people.

30. In what two ways did Christ proclaim the Kingdom of God?

He died, and he told people about it.

31. What kinds of miracles did Christ perform?

Spiritual miracles, things that helped people.

32. Why are Christ's miracles also called "signs"?

They were signs of his divine nature.

33. When some of St. John the Baptist's followers asked Jesus if he was the promised Messiah, what evidence did Christ offer?

    He performed miracles.

34. How is casting out demons a particular sign of the kingdom?

    Evil is cast out of God's kingdom.

35. According to the *Catechism*, no. 550, even though miracles are signs of the Kingdom, what established the Kingdom of God definitively?

    Jesus' resurrection was established it.

36. Was the establishment of the kingdom mainly about eliminating physical evils?

    No, spiritual evils.

37. Why did Christ tell the paralytic first that his sins were forgiven and then heal him?

    He was paralyzed because he was sinful.

38. What were Christ's greatest works?

His miracles of healing.

39. *Critical Thinking*: How did those who witnessed Christ's miracles on a superficial level, i.e., without the eyes of faith or truth-seeking spirits, miss the point of his miraculous works?

They didn't understand what the miracles meant for the world.

40. What is the theme of everything Christ taught?

The theme was loving everyone

41. Of what does the rest of Christ's teaching consist?

His teachings consist of ancient wisdom from God.

42. What was one of the main tools that Christ used to preach about the Kingdom of God?

He used miracles to prove he was the real deal.

43. What is the meaning of the Parable of the Woman Who Leavened Flour?

Anyone can be redeemed

44. How does the Parable of the Lost Sheep relate to redemption?

No matter how far you stray, Jesus will find you.

45. How does the Parable of the Prodigal Son relate to redemption?

No matter what you do, you can be forgiven.

46. What two-part dynamic of redemption exists between the Redeemer and the redeemed?

The Redeemer forgives the redeemed, & they show gratitude

SIDEBAR: THE PARABLE AS A LIGHT TO CONSCIENCE

47. *Critical Thinking*: Choose two of the parables listed in the sidebar "The Parable as a Light to Conscience" (p. 103), read them in a Bible, and then explain in a short paragraph for each what it teaches us about redemption.

The rich man and Lazarus shows that you will get your due after death. Apparently, though, there's no redemption after that. Mercy only stretches so far. The ten talents show that following God's plan will get you rewarded, and not doing so will leave you penniless.

THE "LIGHT" OF THE TRANSFIGURATION

48. How was the Transfiguration a preparation for Christ's Passion and Death?

It reminded us that Christ is God, and he wouldn't be human forever.

49. How did the Transfiguration serve the Apostles later?

They remembered that Jesus was divine.

50. How was the Transfiguration a foretaste of Christ's glory and ours?

We will all be holy and pure some day.

51. *Critical Thinking*: What is the relationship between Christ's Transfiguration and the Cross?

Both lead him to heaven. Back to heaven, from where he briefly left.

ST. FRANCIS DE SALES

52. How was St. Francis de Sales an exemplary priest?

He inspired w/ helped people.

53. How successful was St. Francis in his apostolate?

Not at first, but later.

54. For what book is St. Francis most famous?

The book he wrote about and.

55. After his initial evangelization efforts had failed, with nobody listening to him, to what new tactic did St. Francis resort?

He reached out to new people in different ways.

56. *Critical Thinking*: How is St. Francis a model of perseverance in following God's vocation?

No matter how the world responded, St. Francis continued to do what he knew God wanted him to do.

THE INSTITUTION OF THE EUCHARIST

57. In what sense is the redemption *already accomplished* but *still continuing*?

We were redeemed by Christ on the cross, but we are in constant need of redemption.

58. Why did Christ establish the Church?

To guide and protect us.

59. What is *remembrance* in the liturgical sense?

Remembering things that have happened.

60. According to the *Catechism*, no. 1340, why did Christ choose the Passover meal to institute the Eucharist?

Because it had historical religious significance.

61. Christ identified himself as "the bread of life" (Jn 6:35). When and how did he fulfill his promise to give us his Body and Blood as food and drink?

He died, so his body is dead.

62. What is the legacy of the Last Supper? Consider the three important doctrines Christ imparted during the Last Supper.

eat my body, drink my blood, and love each other.

63. What is the greatest display of charity possible?

Loving another human person.

64. What did Christ indicate that he would lay down for the salvation of every human being?

His life

65. *Critical Thinking*: What is the significance of Christ having washed the feet of his disciples at the Last Supper? Consider the significance not only to the disciples but to all of Christ's disciples throughout the ages.

He serves us, as we should serve him, All of us, throughout the ages

66. What does the Latin phrase *in persona Christi capitis* mean, and to whom does it refer?

Christ was the person of Christ. It refers to Jesus (Christ).

67. In what does the Eucharist enable the faithful to share?

Our love and lives with each other.

68. What did the Last Supper anticipate?

It anticipated the Holy Mass.

69. What does every subsequent Mass anticipate?

Jesus' second coming to save us again.

70. *Critical Thinking*: What is the relationship between the Eucharist and Christ's Sacrifice on the Cross?

The Eucharist is a metaphorical Sacrifice of his body, while the cross was Jesus literally sacrificing his body. The idea of eating it was just us benefiting from it.

CONCLUSION

71. What part of Christ's life do the Luminous Mysteries recall?

    They remender his public minestry.

72. *Luminous* means "shedding or full of light." What is *luminous* about the part of the life of Christ in your answer to the previous question?

    He brings light/joy to the world.

73. How do the Luminous Mysteries relate to the mystery of redemption?

    They show how christ will redeem us with his undending power & love.

74. *Critical Thinking*: Choose one of the Luminous Mysteries, and explain how it relates to the redemption, expounding on how it can unite you more closely to Christ.

    The Proclaimation of the holy thing tells us how to live.

SUPPLEMENTARY READING

75. Use a bullet-point list to summarize the key points of the selection from St. Augustine's *Treatise on the Gospel of John*.

76. Use a bullet-point list to summarize the key points from Pope Benedict XVI's 2008 Homily for Holy Thursday.

textbook p. 119

name _____

REDEMPTION THROUGH THE PASCHAL MYSTERY

INTRODUCTION

1. Why did Christ suffer, die, and rise?

2. Why will Christ come again?

3. In his First Epistle to the Corinthians, how did St. Paul describe the centrality of the Resurrection to the Christian faith?

4. What does it take for us to appropriate the redemption for ourselves?

SIDEBAR: THE DEATH OF CHRIST: WHO IS GUILTY?

5. Were the Jewish authorities responsible for the Death of Christ?

6. Were the Jewish people responsible for the Death of Christ?

7. What was Christ's attitude toward those who condemned him?

8. How have some Christians sinned by blaming the Jews for the Death of Christ?

9. Was Judas responsible for the Death of Christ?

10. What was Judas's punishment for his evil?

11. Were Pontius Pilate and the Roman authorities responsible for the Death of Christ?

12. Who is most responsible for the Death of Christ?

13. *Critical Thinking*: Summarize the *Catechism*, no. 598, and then relate how you personally can make a concerted effort not to continue Christ's Crucifixion throughout the ages.

THE PASSION OF CHRIST: LOVE IN ACTION

14. What good did God bring out of the evil of human sin?

15. According to the *Catechism*, no. 609, what instrument, or "tool," did Christ use to save humanity?

16. What is the Agony in the Garden?

17. What added dramatically to Christ's suffering in the Garden?

18. *Critical Thinking*: What virtue did Christ need especially in praying, "Not as I will, but as thou wilt" (Mt 26:39)?

19. *Critical Thinking*: What can you learn from Christ's Agony in the Garden, especially as it can inform your own life?

20. What are the Suffering Servant songs?

21. What is one example from Isaiah 53:4–6 that prophesied that Christ would suffer for us?

22. What was Christ's scourging?

23. What is the meaning of *Golgotha*, also known as Calvary?

24. When did Christ's Passion reach its climax?

25. When Christ said, "It is finished" (Jn 19:30), what did he mean?

26. *Critical Thinking*: What is the lesson of the story of the Good Thief (cf. the "repentant thief," p. 126)?

27. Mysticism can be defined as the pursuit of union with God by means of contemplation and spiritual discipline; its practice has transcended time, place, and culture. What did Pope Benedict XVI mean when he described Christ's Incarnation and Death on the Cross as "a decisive turning point in the history of mysticism"?

28. According to the *Catechism*, no. 603, what was Christ feeling when he asked, "My God, my God, why have you forsaken me?"

29. What do the Blood and water that flowed from the side of Christ represent?

30. *Critical Thinking*: How were Christ's words on the Cross, "My God, my God, why have you forsaken me?" (Mt 27:46), a declaration of victory? Hint: Read Psalm 22, the beginning of which Christ quoted; consider what the Psalmist revealed about suffering and our relationship with God.

THE SIGNIFICANCE OF CHRIST'S RESURRECTION

31. What did Christ's Resurrection demonstrate?

It demonstrated that he is stronger than death. Nothing can best God.

32. According to the *Catechism*, no. 654, what are the two aspects of the Paschal Mystery?

Suffering & reedemption are the 2 aspects.

33. Did any of the Apostles expect Christ to rise from the dead?

They should have, as he told them so, but they didn't.

34. When did the Apostles come to believe that Christ had risen?

After they had seen him & touched him.

35. According to the *Catechism*, no. 644, what is the status of the hypothesis that the Resurrection was produced by the Apostles' credulity, or faith?

Not believed by many, as there faith was not super strong.

36. What was Christ's resurrected Body like?

It looked slightly warped, very bright & shinny.

37. *Critical Thinking*: Christ's post-Resurrection encounter with two disciples on the road to Emmaus is mentioned on page 129; read the entire account (cf. Lk 24:13–33) in a Bible. What happened on the road to Emmaus, and why is it significant? Hint: Consider the confirmation of the Resurrection and the role of the Eucharist.

It confirmed the Jesus had been resurrected. He continued the Eucharist, such that his death did not end his ministry.

38. What is an example of Christ foretelling his Resurrection directly?

He said that he would raise the temple again in 3 days.

39. How did Christ use metaphors to foretell his Resurrection?

He used metaphors to help us understand something so awe-inspiring it borders on inconceivable

40. What did Christ do after his Death and before his Resurrection?

He descended into Hell.

41. What was the state of the just, or holy, souls who had died before Christ's Death, and how was their state changed by Christ's Passion and Death? Hint: Read the *Catechism*, nos. 633 and 634 on page 147.

They stayed in a state of limbo, known as "Abraham's bosom."

OUR PARTICIPATION IN THE MYSTERY OF REDEMPTION

42. For what two tasks is the Church the instrument?

43. By what primary means can people receive the grace of the redemption? Give the basic definition according to the *Catechism*, no. 1131.

44. What does it mean to say that the Sacraments are effective signs that give grace?

45. What is necessary on our part for the Sacraments to have their intended effect?

SIDEBAR: THE SEVEN SACRAMENTS

46. What is the connection between the Resurrection, the Sacrament of Penance and Reconciliation, and the redemption? Hint: Read the sources given for the Sacrament of Penance and Reconciliation on page 135.

47. *Critical Thinking*: How is the Church the Sacrament of Salvation? Hint: Focus on how the Church can be considered a *sacrament*, and then focus on her mission.

THE REDEMPTIVE MEANING OF THE ASCENSION

48. How do the Incarnation and the Ascension relate?

One makes Jesus a human, and the other takes him back to heaven

49. What is the *Parousia*?

Jesus' second coming

50. How is the Ascension linked to the Resurrection?

After the Resurrection, he went to Hell. Now he goes to heaven.

51. What does it mean to say that the Ascension marks the entrance of Christ's humanity into heaven so we can enter in our humanity?

The human christ, goes to heaven so we can too.

52. What is the significance of Christ returning to the "right hand of God," and what does this position represent?

It represents how he helps God keep in touch with us.

53. At the Ascension how did Christ promise to be with us always until the end of time?

He said he would always be with us.

54. What are some of the graces we can receive through the Holy Spirit?

Faith, hope, and charity.

55. According to the *Catechism*, no. 788, how is Christ more accessible to us now than before his Ascension?

Now he is with God in heaven, and can be with us more spiritually and readily before.

56. What happened at Pentecost, and what effects did it have on the Apostles?

The Apostles were sent out to be missionaries

57. What does the Holy Spirit continue to do for the Church's mission?

It guides the church and brings people into the holy faith.

58. What does it mean to say that the Ascension anticipates our own resurrection?

we'll all go to heaven after we die and live with God forever.

59. What is the Assumption?

*When Mary was taken up, body
and soul, to heaven.*

60. What is another name for the Assumption?

*The crowning of Mary
Queen of Heaven*

61. How does the Blessed Virgin Mary's Assumption anticipate the resurrection of all the faithful?

*If we are faithful and good like her, we
will follow her to heaven.*

SIDEBAR: ST. JOAN OF ARC

62. Who was St. Joan of Arc?

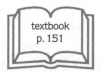

Chapter 6

OUR RESPONSE TO THE GIFT OF REDEMPTION

INTRODUCTION

1. In what sense is the redemption both *rooted in time* and *timeless*?

2. Why is the redemption sometimes described as *superabundant*?

3. In what sense do we *earn* redemption, and in what sense do we *not earn* redemption?

4. Why are we able to reject the gift of redemption?

GOD'S DESIRE FOR US: HAPPINESS AND HOLINESS

5. For what kind of happiness has God redeemed us?

6. What is ultimate human failure?

7. According to St. Augustine, why does every human being have a restless heart?

8. How does the call to happiness relate to the call to holiness?

9. *Critical Thinking*: God is All-good and created human beings to be happy with him forever. Why, then, did he allow Adam and Eve to sin and thus bring sin and death into the world?

10. According to the Second Vatican Council, what is the fundamental Christian vocation?

11. We are called to perfect holiness, but is perfect holiness possible for a human being?

12. *Critical Thinking*: How ought every person to respond to God's universal call to holiness? Give some examples of its application.

REDEMPTION, GRACE, AND FREE WILL

13. What natural gifts set human beings apart from all other natural creatures?

14. According to the *Catechism*, no. 1704, what can reason and free will do?

15. How do we receive the grace of the redemption first?

16. Why is Baptism necessary for salvation?

17. What are some effects of Baptism?

18. What is concupiscence?

19. What is mortal sin, and how can it be forgiven?

20. Is it possible for a baptized person to avoid mortal sin always?

SIDEBAR: OBJECTIVE AND SUBJECTIVE REDEMPTION

21. *Critical Thinking*: What role does an individual person play with regard to his or her salvation?

PRACTICING THE THEOLOGICAL VIRTUES

22. How can we grow in holiness?

23. What is a virtue?

24. How does practicing the virtues make us more like God?

25. What is *theological* about the theological virtues?

26. How do people receive the theological virtues?

27. What is faith, and on what authority do we accept truths of faith?

28. *Critical Thinking*: In addition to believing what God has revealed through his Church, what else is required for the practice of the theological virtue of faith?

29. How do faith and reason interrelate?

30. What is hope?

31. What is charity?

32. Of the three theological virtues, which is the most important?

33. *Critical Thinking*: How is it possible for a person to love as Christ loved?

34. What are natural virtues?

35. What are the most notable supernatural virtues?

SIDEBAR: AIDS AND MARKS OF CHRISTIAN VIRTUES: THE GIFTS AND FRUITS OF THE HOLY SPIRIT

36. Generally speaking, what are the gifts of the Holy Spirit?

37. What do the gifts of the Holy Spirit do?

38. What does the gift of wisdom do?

39. What does the gift of understanding do?

40. What does the gift of counsel do?

41. What does the gift of fortitude do?

42. What does the gift of piety do?

43. What does the gift of fear of the Lord do?

44. Which gifts of the Holy Spirit act on the intellect?

45. Which gifts of the Holy Spirit act on the will?

46. Generally speaking, what are the fruits of the Holy Spirit?

47. In what sense are there more than twelve fruits of the Holy Spirit?

THE IMITATION OF CHRIST

48. What is our lifelong mission in relation to Christ?

49. According to Christ, how can we show that we love him?

50. What did Christ tell the rich young man to do when he expressed a desire to be perfect?

51. What is the first and greatest Commandment, according to Christ?

52. What is the second greatest Commandment, according to Christ?

53. Can a person become holy merely by obeying Christ?

54. How can grace and our cooperation with grace transform us into saints?

LIVING OUT GOD'S CALL TO HOLINESS

55. What are repentance and conversion?

56. How is conversion a response to something supremely good?

57. What "data" do our consciences use to guide us?

58. How does conscience relate to conversion?

59. Why is the verdict of conscience a "pledge of conversion and hope" (CCC 1797) for the person who has done evil?

60. How do we educate our consciences?

61. Why does a person need an interior life in order to follow his or her conscience, and what is important to do to foster an interior life?

62. What is an examination of conscience, and what is its purpose?

63. Why is it wise to make an examination of conscience every night and before going to Confession?

64. What is the basis of the Christian moral life?

65. What is natural law?

66. Why is the moral law for everyone?

67. Why do people misunderstand the moral law sometimes?

68. What is the Decalogue?

69. How did Christ underscore the Ten Commandments with two other Commandments?

70. How did Christ perfect the moral law?

71. What do the Beatitudes describe?

72. What does *beatitude* mean?

73. According to the Beatitudes, what are the conditions for human perfection and lasting happiness?

74. According to the *Catechism*, no. 1717, of what do the Beatitudes give us a portrait?

75. What is the role of the Church on earth?

76. According to the *Catechism*, no. 824, how do we become holy by means of the Church?

77. What is the process of "building up the Church"?

78. What is the "battle" of prayer?

79. How does suffering correspond to personal holiness?

80. What is our duty in regard to the Kingdom of God on earth?

81. *Critical Thinking*: What do the lives of the saints reveal about the holiness of the Church? Hint: Consider the Church's sacramental life as a conduit to holiness.

82. What does the Parable of the Three Stewards reveal about building up the Kingdom of God on earth?

83. Historically, how has the Church loved those in need?

84. What is the purpose of the corporal and spiritual works of mercy?

85. What, in general, are the corporal works of mercy? Then list them.

86. What, in general, are the spiritual works of mercy? Then list them.

87. *Critical Thinking*: The painting by Niccolo depicts St. Lawrence distributing alms to the poor (p. 164). Read a short biography of the life of St. Lawrence and write a brief biographical sketch of his life. Include what he described to be the Church's "treasure," what kind of martyrdom he endured, and what he may have said as he was being martyred.

88. Is it enough to believe in Christ?

89. What must a person do before trying to evangelize others?

90. What is the meaning of the word *martyr*?

91. What did St. Francis of Assisi mean when he said, "Preach the gospel at all times; if necessary, use words"?

92. According to Pope St. John Paul II, how will people be recognized as true disciples of Christ, and what kind of love did he encourage young people to live out?

93. What role does God give human beings within creation?

94. What problem exists today in regard to the principle that "the goods of creation are destined for the whole human race"?

95. What is problematic with the excessive consumption of natural resources?

96. According to the *Catechism*, no. 2415, what limits the right of a person to use creation?

SIDEBAR: THE PRECEPTS OF THE CHURCH

97. What, in general, are the Precepts of the Church?

98. What force do the Precepts of the Church have for Catholics?

99. Can the Church change her Precepts?

100. *Critical Thinking*: The Ten Commandments are articulations of natural law, binding on everyone, knowable by reason, and unchangeable. The Precepts of the Church are in accord with the natural law but they are binding on Catholics only; they are perfectly reasonable in helping the faithful live out their Christian lives. Choose one of the Commandment and one of the Precepts of the Church and explain how the Commandment is reasonable to help a person to live a good moral life and how the precept is reasonable to help a person to live a good Christian life.

THE LAST THINGS

101. What are the "Last Things"?

102. What does the redemption promise in regard to death?

103. Why is death a hopeful prospect for every Christian?

104. What will be the final act of the redemption?

105. What is the result of the Particular Judgment?

106. Are heaven, purgatory, and hell places?

107. According to the *Catechism*, nos. 678–679, what kinds of questions will be answered at the General Judgment?

108. Why was Gehenna an apt image of damnation?

109. What is hell, how does a soul get to that state, and who is responsible for this final destination?

110. At death and the Particular Judgment, does the soul of every person who has died in a state of grace go directly to heaven?

111. Why is purgatory likened to fire?

112. What is the essence of the pain of purgatory?

113. What is the Church's attitude toward the souls in purgatory?

114. How does heaven relate to the idea of happiness?

115. According to the *Catechism*, no. 1026 (p. 182), what does it take to become a partner with God in heaven?

116. What is the most important thing that we can do to attain heaven despite our personal failures?

117. What should be our lifelong "project"?

SIDEBAR: ST. ROSE PHILIPPINE DUCHESNE

118.What political upheaval interrupted St. Rose Philippine Duchesne's religious vocation, and how?

119.What was St. Rose's life's work, and how was it saintly?

CONCLUSION

120.Toward what is the goal of love of neighbor through service ordered?

121.According to the Second Vatican Council, how do we "find" ourselves fully?

122. *Critical Thinking*: In regard to our exalted stature and every human being's need to serve others, the Fathers of the Second Vatican Council wrote, "Man, who is the only creature on earth which God willed for itself, cannot fully find himself except through a sincere gift of himself" (*GS* 24). What does this statement mean, taking into account what it means to be willed for itself, to find oneself fully, and to make a sincere gift of self? How can you make a gift of yourself in your present circumstances?

SUPPLEMENTARY READING

123. According to St. Ephrem, why did Christ not reveal the exact time of his Second Coming?

124. Explain St. Maximus the Confessor's views on charity.

125. What does *Lumen Gentium*, no. 40, teach us about the universal call to holiness?

textbook p. 185

Chapter 7

PRAYER IN THE LIFE OF A BELIEVER

INTRODUCTION

1. How can we encounter the God of redemption, with whom we are called to have an intimate relationship?

2. In what one activity did all the saints in the history of the Church share, no matter how diverse their ministries were?

PRAYER IS A DIALOGUE WITH GOD

3. What is a simple definition of prayer?

4. How are the effects of a regular prayer life manifested?

5. What is the highest form of prayer to which the Church calls the faithful, and how does it relate to the mystery of redemption?

6. How is prayer on earth related to prayer in heaven?

7. According to the *Catechism*, no. 2560, why does God "thirst" for us, and how does this relate to prayer?

8. *Critical Thinking*: How does grace respond to the innate human desire for God, which St. Augustine's quote about his restless heart expressed so well?

SCRIPTURE AS A SOURCE OF PRAYER

9. What is one of the main ways to hear God speak?

10. Why is it important to read the Scriptures prayerfully?

11. What is the place of the Psalms in Christian prayer?

12. What is the source of key traditional prayers of the Church, as well as the great majority of the prayers of the Mass and of other Church liturgies?

13. What is the source of the entire Liturgy of the Word in the Mass?

14. On what is the Liturgy of the Hours based primarily?

SCRIPTURE IN THE LITURGY OF THE WORD

15. What were the two parts of the Christian liturgy in the first centuries of the Church?

16. What are these two parts of the Mass called today?

17. Which scriptural readings does the Liturgy of the Word include on Sundays and Holy Days of Obligation?

18. What is the Lectionary?

19. What is the relationship among any day's selection of Lectionary readings for the Mass?

20. What is a great way to hear the Sacred Scriptures constantly in a prayerful context?

21. According to the *Catechism*, no. 1100, what is the source of all the other parts of the Mass?

SCRIPTURE IN THE LITURGY OF THE HOURS

22. What benefits can be gained from the "rhythm of prayer" fostered by the Liturgy of the Hours?

23. What comprises the Liturgy of the Hours?

24. What comprises the Office of Readings?

SIDEBAR: REFLECTIONS ON THE HAIL MARY FROM THE CATECHISM OF THE CATHOLIC CHURCH

25. Who greeted the Blessed Virgin Mary at the Annunciation?

26. How is the Blessed Virgin Mary "full of grace"?

27. Why is the Blessed Virgin Mary blessed among women?

28. How is the Blessed Virgin Mary our Mother?

29. How should the Blessed Virgin Mary's response to the Archangel Gabriel be our prayer?

30. Why should we ask the Blessed Virgin Mary to pray for us sinners?

LECTIO DIVINA

31. What is the literal meaning of *lectio divina*, and what is it?

Lectio Divina means the divine rector.

32. How did the *lectio divina* method of prayer develop?

People started doing it to get closer to god.

33. *Critical Thinking*: Another method of meditation was developed in the sixteenth century by St. Ignatius Loyola, the founder of the Jesuits. Ignatian meditation, as it is called, makes creative use of a person's imagination through "visualization," which engages all of the senses in order to help a person imagine that he or she is in a given situation in order to experience it more deeply. The senses thus inform the soul in situations such as a biblical scene, a work of sacred art, or even poetry. The practitioner of Ignatian meditation asks such questions as the following:

- What can I hear?
- What can I see?
- What can I smell?
- What can I touch?
- What can I taste?

Take a few minutes to practice Ignatian meditation using the painting *The Angelus* by Millet (p. 202), which depicts a French farm couple having just heard the church bells in the background, prompting them to bow their heads to pray the *Angelus* (p. 154) at the end of their workday. Write down what you can imagine hearing, seeing, smelling, touching, and even tasting. Think about what kind of people they might be. Imagine treading across the furrowed field and speaking with them, maybe offering to lend them a hand. The key thing is to be imaginative. Then relate how this Ignatian meditation has affected your appreciation of the scene depicted.

Ignatian meditation lets you enter a scene
ud really Feel the emotion that go with it.

EXPRESSIONS OF PRAYER

34. What is vocal prayer?

Praying out loud

35. What is spontaneous vocal prayer?

Saying a prayer that you make up.

36. Why is vocal prayer important in the life of a faithful Christian?

It lets you share your prayers w/a community.

37. According to the *Catechism*, no. 2705, why is it good to use texts to assist our meditation?

It helps us return to the root of the prayer.

38. According to the *Catechism*, no. 2705, what unwritten "texts" can be the basis of our meditation?

Prayers written in our heads, stories we've heard.

39. How does the Holy Rosary combine both vocal prayer and meditation?

You meditate on the mysteries and pray out loud.

40. According to the *Catechism*, no. 2708, what is the essence of meditative prayer?

It is raising your mind to God.

41. What is the effect of contemplative prayer on the soul?

It helps our souls grow closer to god.

FORMS OF PRAYER

42. What is a prayer of blessing?

43. What is a prayer of adoration, and how is it *relational* between God and the person praying?

44. What is a prayer of petition?

45. Will God answer our prayers of petition?

46. *Critical Thinking*: Does God answer every prayer? Explain.

47. Why is it appropriate to ask God for favors?

48. What is a prayer of intercession?

49. What is our motive for intercessory prayer?

50. How is intercessory prayer Christlike?

51. Who can intercede for us?

52. What is a prayer of thanksgiving?

53. What is a prayer of praise?

54. What is a prayer of contrition?

DIFFICULTIES IN PRAYER

55. Should we be surprised if prayer is ever hard to do? Why is it a struggle?

56. How can having a place set aside for prayer eliminate some distractions?

57. According to the *Catechism*, no. 2729, how can distractions be a source of prayer?

58. How can praying the Rosary be an example of vocal prayer leading into meditation?

59. Who are two saints who faced difficulties in prayer, especially dryness in their relationship with God? What did they feel, despite not losing their faith?

60. What is the antidote to dryness in prayer?

TEMPTATIONS IN PRAYER

61. In asking for things, how should we approach God?

62. What is a vital key to successful prayer?

63. According to the *Catechism*, no. 2741, what gift do we receive in prayer always?

64. *Critical Thinking*: Describe your ideal prayer situation, that is, the one most conducive for dialogue with God. Include the setting, the time, and whether you will use any object of devotion—for example, a crucifix or an object of sacred art such as an icon—to focus your attention on God.

THE MODEL OF PERFECT PRAYER

65. According to Pope Benedict XVI, why does the Sermon on the Mount include a teaching about prayer?

66. Why is the *Lord's Prayer* a perfect prayer?

67. According to the *Catechism*, no. 2763, what does the *Lord's Prayer* reveal about prayer of petition?

68. What is the difference between the way Christ referred to the Father and the way he taught his disciples to refer to the Father?

69. What does calling upon God as "our" Father emphasize?

70. With which Commandment is, "Hallowed be thy name," associated most closely?

71. According to St. Matthew (6:33), what is the key to getting everything we want in life?

72. Which law of Christ shows us the way to live in the Kingdom of God?

73. What is the Kingdom of God essentially?

74. *Critical Thinking*: What does it mean to pray, "Thy kingdom come"?

75. According to Pope Benedict XVI, how does earth become heaven?

76. Understanding Christ's teachings is important to discerning God's will for our lives. How can we come to a greater understanding of them?

77. Should we worry about having enough material things? According to Pope Benedict XVI, how does prayer factor into this consideration?

78. What is the "hidden" meaning of "our daily bread"?

79. What does the petition to "forgive us" call us to do?

80. How do our temptations relate to Christ's?

81. What is our internal source of temptation?

82. What is positive about every temptation?

83. *Critical Thinking*: English translations of the *Lord's Prayer* from the original Greek usually end this perfect prayer with, "Deliver us from evil," rather than, "Deliver us from the evil one." How does this change your understanding of the meaning of the *Lord's Prayer* as a whole?

84. What does our use of "Amen" at the end of prayers express?

85. How did Christ teach his disciples to pray by example?

86. How did Christ, in his eagerness and commitment to speak with the Father, reveal the importance of the power of prayer?

87. According to the *Catechism*, no. 2765, how is Christ the "model of our prayer"?

SIDEBAR: ST. BENEDICT OF NURSIA

88. Who was St. Benedict of Nursia, and why is he important?

89. What is a *scriptorium* (*scriptoria* is the plural), and what did monks do in them?

SUPPLEMENTARY READINGS

90. According to St. Cyprian of Carthage, what has the Lord given us to help us toward salvation?

91. According to Pope Benedict XVI, what did the Second Vatican Council, through the document *Dei Verbum*, do in terms of Scripture and prayer?

92. According to Pope Benedict XVI, is scriptural prayer a purely private matter?

93. According to Pope Benedict XVI, what is the privileged place for the prayerful reading of Scripture, and why is it so?

94. According to Pope Benedict XVI, how does the prayerful reading of Scripture in general—and the practice of *lectio divina* in particular—relate to the proclamation of the Word in the liturgy?

95. *Critical Thinking*: Study the fresco of *The Ascension* by Giotto (p. 212). Identify the elements from St. Luke's account of Christ's Ascension (cf. Acts 1:9–11) that are depicted in this scene. Then spend a few minutes practicing *lectio divina* (cf. p. 192 of the text) on this text or practicing Ignatian meditation (cf. question 33, p. 128 of this *Student Workbook*) on this fresco; record some of your thoughts in a private location such as a notebook or diary.

No Material on This Page

textbook
p.213

Appendix

CHALLENGES TO FAITH IN THE REDEMPTION

INTRODUCTION

1. What is apologetics?

2. How does a Catholic apologist approach a *natural* truth that is called into question?

3. How does a Catholic apologist approach a *supernatural* mystery that is called into question?

1. WHY WOULD GOD THE FATHER ALLOW HIS SON, JESUS, TO SUFFER AND DIE THE WAY HE DID (CCC 599–609)?

4. What short answer does the Gospel of St. John provide to the question, "Why would God the Father allow his Son to undergo what he suffered?"

5. What is the central mystery of redemption?

6. What did God foresee about human beings even before he created them?

7. What is the general condition of human beings under Original Sin?

8. What two deaths are consequences of sin?

9. What remote preparation for the redemption is recounted in the Old Testament?

10. What exemplifies Christ's love for us?

11. What exemplifies the love we are called to show one another?

12. According to the *Catechism*, no. 402, what parallel exists between Adam and Christ?

13. *Critical Thinking*: Study the pulpit carved by Verbruggen, which depicts *Adam and Eve Banished from Paradise* (p. 215). How does it manifest the consequences of Original Sin?

2. WHY ARE FOLLOWERS OF JESUS CHRIST SOMETIMES SO WILLING TO MAKE SACRIFICES AND TO ACCEPT PAIN AND SUFFERING, ESPECIALLY IN WITNESS TO CHRIST AND THEIR FAITH?

14. Why, in short, are followers of Christ often willing to suffer for him?

15. According to the *Catechism*, no. 618, why are we able to be "partners" with Christ in suffering?

16. According to his Epistle to the Philippians (3:8, 10–11; p. 218), why was St. Paul willing to suffer the loss of all things?

17. *Critical Thinking*: The world tends to view suffering as something to be avoided at all costs. Suffering, when it does come, is pitied and frowned upon as tragic and completely useless. Spend a few minutes practicing *lectio divina* (cf. p. 192 of the text) or practicing Ignatian meditation (cf. question 33, p. 128 of this *Student Workbook*) on St. Paul's attitude toward suffering in Colossians 1:24.

    a. How do you think you will respond to suffering the next time it comes your way? Record some of your thoughts in a private location such as a notebook or diary.

    b. Recall a time you suffered in the past but treated it from the world's point of view. How might you have responded differently if you had St. Paul's attitude in mind? Is there anything you can do to retroactively make that suffering redemptive? Record some of your thoughts in a private location such as a notebook or diary.

3. ISN'T MAKING SACRIFICES AND ENDURING SUFFERING A SIGN OF WEAKNESS (CCC 1808, 1831)?

18. What is the basic answer to the objection that making sacrifices and enduring suffering is a sign of weakness?

19. What analogy exists between athletes or professionals in the workplace and the Christian life?

20. In what sense *do we not* and in what sense *do we* save ourselves?

21. What is the gift of redemption, which Christ offers us?

22. Why is it impossible to avoid sacrifice when we choose to follow Christ?

4. IN THE END, ISN'T IT REALLY ONLY THE FINAL RESULT THAT MATTERS?

23. What three factors must be considered in judging the morality of an act?

24. What is the *object* of an act?

25. What must both the object and the act be in themselves in order for the act to be morally good?

26. What is an example of an objectively good act?

27. If the object of an act is objectively evil, is that act good, evil, or can its goodness or evilness not be determined?

28. What are examples of objectively evil acts in themselves?

29. What is the *intention* of an act?

30. For an act to be completely virtuous, what must a person's *intention* be?

31. Imagine that a person has given shelter to a homeless person.
    a. What is an example of a good intention for this act?

    b. What is an example of a bad intention for this act?

32. What are the *circumstances* of an act?

33. According to the *Catechism*, no. 1756, what are some examples of circumstances that affect the moral gravity of an act?

34. What moral judgment about another person can we *not* make?

35. What moral judgment about another is legitimate to make?

36. What must guide us when we evaluate the behavior of others, and how can we do this?

37. *Critical Thinking*: "Follow your conscience" is advice that is given often but misunderstood almost as often. What kind of conscience helps a person to perform a morally good act, i.e., an act that is good in its *object* and in its *intention*?

CATHOLIC PRAYERS AND DEVOTIONS

In any endeavor, there are certain basics that must be learned, memorized, and internalized. These prayers and devotions are fundamental to the life of an active, practicing Catholic.

The Ten Commandments

1. I am the LORD your God: you shall not have strange gods before me.
2. You shall not take the name of the LORD your God in vain.
3. Remember to keep holy the LORD's Day.
4. Honor your father and your mother.
5. You shall not kill.
6. You shall not commit adultery.
7. You shall not steal.
8. You shall not bear false witness against your neighbor.
9. You shall not covet your neighbor's wife.
10. You shall not covet your neighbor's goods.

The Precepts of the Church   (CCC 2042–2043)

1. You shall attend Mass on Sundays and holy days of obligation and rest from servile labor.
2. You shall confess your sins at least once a year.
3. You shall receive the sacrament of the Eucharist at least during the Easter season.
4. You shall observe the days of fasting and abstinence established by the Church.
5. You shall help to provide for the needs of the Church.

The Corporal Works of Mercy

- Feeding the hungry
- Giving drink to the thirsty
- Clothing the naked
- Sheltering the homeless
- Visiting the sick
- Visiting the imprisoned
- Burying the dead

The Spiritual Works of Mercy

- Counseling the doubtful
- Instructing the ignorant
- Admonishing sinners
- Comforting the afflicted
- Forgiving offenses
- Bearing wrongs patiently
- Praying for the living and the dead

The Gifts of the Holy Spirit

- Wisdom
- Understanding
- Counsel
- Fortitude
- Knowledge
- Piety
- Fear of the Lord

Theological Virtues

- Faith
- Hope
- Charity

The Sins that Cry to Heaven

- The murder of the innocent (cf. Gn 4:10)
- Homosexual behavior (cf. Gn 18:20, 19:13)
- The enslavement of people (cf. Ex 3:7–10)
- Oppression of the widow, orphan, or alien (cf. Ex 22:21–24)
- Withholding wages from the laborer (cf. Dt 24:14–15)

"The catechetical tradition also recalls that there are '*sins that cry to heaven*': the blood of Abel, the sin of the Sodomites, the cry of the people oppressed in Egypt, the cry of the foreigner, the widow, and the orphan, injustice to the wage earner" (CCC 1867).

Capital Sins

- Pride
- Covetousness
- Lust
- Anger
- Gluttony
- Envy
- Sloth

Opposed Virtues

- Humility
- Liberality
- Chastity
- Meekness
- Temperance
- Brotherly love
- Diligence

Cardinal Virtues

- Prudence
- Justice
- Fortitude
- Temperance

The Beatitudes   (Mt 5:3–12)

- Blessed are the poor in spirit, for theirs is the kingdom of heaven.
- Blessed are those who mourn, for they shall be comforted.
- Blessed are the meek, for they shall inherit the earth.
- Blessed are those who hunger and thirst for righteousness, for they shall be satisfied.
- Blessed are the merciful, for they shall obtain mercy.
- Blessed are the pure of heart, for they shall see God.
- Blessed are the peacemakers, for they shall be called sons of God.
- Blessed are those who are persecuted for righteousness' sake, for theirs is the kingdom of heaven.
- Blessed are you when men revile you and persecute you and utter all kinds of evil against you falsely on my account. Rejoice and be glad, for your reward is great in heaven.

The Sign of the Cross

In the name of the Father, and of the Son, and of the Holy Spirit. Amen.

The Lord's Prayer

Our Father, who art in heaven, hallowed be thy name. Thy kingdom come; thy will be done on earth as it is in heaven. Give us this day our daily bread; and forgive us our trespasses as we forgive those who trespass against us; and lead us not into temptation, but deliver us from evil. Amen.

The Hail Mary

Hail, Mary, full of grace, the Lord is with you; blessed are you among women, and blessed is the fruit of your womb, Jesus. Holy Mary, Mother of God, pray for us sinners, now and at the hour of our death. Amen.

The Glory Be (The Doxology)

Glory be to the Father, and to the Son, and to the Holy Spirit. As it was in the beginning, is now, and ever shall be, world without end. Amen.

Morning Offering

O Jesus, through the Immaculate Heart of Mary, I offer you my prayers, works, joys, and sufferings of this day for all the intentions of your Sacred Heart, in union with the Holy Sacrifice of the Mass throughout the world, in thanksgiving for your favors, in reparation for my sins, for the intentions of all my relatives and friends, and in particular for the intentions of the Holy Father. Amen.

Consecration to the Blessed Virgin Mary

My Queen and my Mother, I give myself entirely to you, and, in proof of my affection, I give you my eyes, my ears, my tongue, my heart, my whole being without reserve. Since I am your own, keep me and guard me as your property and possession. Amen.

Act of Faith

O my God, I firmly believe that you are one God in three divine Persons, Father, Son, and Holy Spirit; I believe that your divine Son became man and died for our sins, and that he shall come to judge the living and the dead. I believe these and all the truths that the holy Catholic Church teaches, because you have revealed them, who can neither deceive nor be deceived.

Act of Hope

O my God, relying on your almighty power and infinite mercy and promises, I hope to obtain pardon for my sins, the help of your grace, and life everlasting, through the merits of Jesus Christ, my Lord and Redeemer.

Act of Charity

O my God, I love you above all things, with my whole heart and soul, because you are all-good and worthy of all love. I love my neighbor as myself for the love of you. I forgive all who have injured me and ask pardon of all whom I have injured.

Prayer to One's Guardian Angel

Angel of God, my guardian dear, to whom God's love commits me here, ever this day (night) be at my side, to light and guard, to rule and guide. Amen.

The *Angelus*   (*Said outside the Easter Season*)

℣. The angel of the Lord declared unto Mary;

℞. And she conceived by the Holy Spirit.

Hail Mary . . .

℣. Behold the handmaid of the Lord.

℞. Be it done unto me according to your word.

Hail Mary . . .

℣. And the Word was made flesh,

℞. And dwelt among us.

Hail Mary . . .

℣. Pray for us, O holy Mother of God.

℞. That we may be made worthy of the promises of Christ.

℣. Let us pray.
Pour forth we beseech you, O Lord, your grace into our hearts, that we, to whom the Incarnation of Christ, your Son, was made known by the message of an angel, may by his Passion and Cross be brought to the glory of his Resurrection, through the same Christ our Lord.

℞. Amen.

Regina Cæli   (*Said during the Easter Season*)

℣. Queen of heaven, rejoice! Alleluia.

℞. For he whom you did merit to bear. Alleluia.

℣. Has risen, as he said. Alleluia.

℞. Pray for us to God. Alleluia.

℣. Rejoice and be glad, O Virgin Mary. Alleluia.

℞. For the Lord is truly risen. Alleluia.

℣. Let us pray.
O God who gave joy to the world through the Resurrection of your Son, our Lord Jesus Christ, grant, we beseech you, that through the intercession of the Virgin Mary, his Mother, we may obtain the joys of everlasting life, through the same Christ our Lord.

℞. Amen.

Prayer to the Holy Spirit

℣. Come, O Holy Spirit, fill the hearts of your faithful and enkindle in them the fire of your love. Send forth your Spirit, and they shall be created.

℞. And you shall renew the face of the earth.

℣. Let us pray.
O God, who has taught the hearts of the faithful by the light of the Holy Spirit, grant that by the gift of the same Spirit we may be always truly wise and ever rejoice in his consolation. Through Christ our Lord.

℞. Amen

Eternal Rest

℣. Eternal rest grant unto them (him/her), O Lord,

℞. And let perpetual light shine upon them (him/her).

℣. May they (he/she) rest in peace.

℞. Amen.

℣. May their (his/her) soul(s) and the souls of all the faithful departed, through the mercy of God, rest in peace.

℞. Amen.

Blessing Before a Meal

Bless us, O Lord, and these your gifts, which we are about to receive from your bounty, through Christ our Lord. Amen.

Thanksgiving After a Meal

We give you thanks, almighty God, for all your benefits, who live and reign forever and ever. [And may the souls of the faithful departed, through the mercy of God, rest in peace.] Amen.

The Apostles' Creed

I believe in God,
the Father almighty,
Creator of heaven and earth,
and in Jesus Christ, his only Son, our Lord,
who was conceived by the Holy Spirit,
born of the Virgin Mary,
suffered under Pontius Pilate,
was crucified, died and was buried;
he descended into hell;
on the third day he rose again from the dead;
he ascended into heaven,
and is seated at the right hand
    of God the Father almighty;
from there he will come to judge
    the living and the dead.

I believe in the Holy Spirit,
the holy catholic Church,
the communion of saints,
the forgiveness of sins,
the resurrection of the body,
and life everlasting. Amen.

Fatima Prayer

O my Jesus, forgive us our sins, save us from the fire of hell, draw all souls to heaven, especially those who are in most need of your mercy. Amen.

Hail Holy Queen

Hail, holy Queen, Mother of mercy, our life, our sweetness, and our hope. To you do we cry, poor banished children of Eve. To you do we send up our sighs, mourning and weeping in this valley of tears. Turn then, most gracious Advocate, your eyes of mercy towards us, and after this exile show unto us the blessed fruit of your womb, Jesus. O clement, O loving, O sweet Virgin Mary.

℣. Pray for us, O holy Mother of God.

℟. That we may be made worthy of the promises of Christ.

Rosary Prayer

O God, whose Only-Begotten Son, by his Life, Death, and Resurrection, has purchased for us the rewards of eternal life; grant, we beseech you, that we, who meditate on these mysteries of the most holy Rosary of the Blessed Virgin Mary, may imitate what they contain, and obtain what they promise. Through Christ our Lord. Amen.

The *Memorare*

Remember, O most gracious Virgin Mary, that never was it known that anyone who fled to your protection, implored your help, or sought your intercession was left unaided. Inspired with this confidence, I fly unto you, O Virgin of virgins, my Mother. To you I come, before you I stand, sinful and sorrowful. O Mother of the Word incarnate, despise not my petitions, but in your mercy hear and answer me. Amen.

Act of Contrition

O my God, I am heartily sorry for having offended you, and I detest all my sins, because I dread the loss of heaven and the pains of hell; but most of all because they offend you, my God, who are all-good and deserving of all of my love. I firmly resolve, with the help of your grace, to confess my sins, to do penance, and to amend my life. Amen.

Prayer to St. Michael

Saint Michael the archangel, defend us in battle; be our defense against the wickedness and snares of the Devil. May God rebuke him, we humbly pray. And do you, O prince of the heavenly host, by the power of God thrust into hell Satan and all the evil spirits who prowl about the world for the ruin of souls. Amen.

How to Pray the Rosary

1. Holding the Crucifix in your hand, make the Sign of the Cross and pray the Apostles' Creed.
2. On the first bead after the Crucifix, pray the Our Father.
3. Pray one Hail Mary on each of the next three beads, asking God to increase faith, hope, and charity in your life.
4. On the bead after these three, pray the Glory Be, announce the First Mystery, and pray the Our Father.
5. Pray one Hail Mary for each of the ten following beads, and end them by praying the Glory Be and the Fatima Prayer.
6. Announce the Second Mystery and repeat steps four and five. Do the same for the Third, Fourth, and Fifth Mysteries.
7. After the Fatima Prayer for the Fifth Mystery, pray the Hail Holy Queen, the Rosary Prayer, and end with the Sign of the Cross.

The Joyful Mysteries

1. The Annunciation   (Lk 1:26–38)
2. The Visitation   (Lk 1:39–56)
3. The Nativity   (Lk 2:1–20)
4. The Presentation   (Lk 2:22–38)
5. The Finding of Jesus in the Temple   (Lk 2:41–51)

The Luminous Mysteries

1. The Baptism of Christ in the Jordan   (Mk 1:9–11)
2. The Manifestation of Christ at the Wedding of Cana   (Jn 2:1–12)
3. The Proclamation of the Kingdom of God, with His Call to Conversion   (Mk 1:14–15)
4. The Transfiguration   (Mk 9:2–8)
5. The Institution of the Eucharist   (Mk 14:22–26)

The Sorrowful Mysteries

1. The Agony in the Garden   (Mt 26:36–46)
2. The Scourging at the Pillar   (Jn 19:1)
3. The Crowning with Thorns   (Mt 27:29)
4. The Carrying of the Cross   (Jn 19:16–17)
5. The Crucifixion   (Jn 19:18–30)

The Glorious Mysteries

1. The Resurrection   (Mk 16:1–8)
2. The Ascension   (Lk 24:50–52)
3. The Descent of the Holy Spirit   (Acts 2:1–13)
4. The Assumption   (Ps 16:10)
5. The Coronation of the Blessed Virgin Mary   (Rev 12:1–2)

The Stations of the Cross

Traditional

1. Jesus Is Condemned to Death
2. Jesus Takes Up His Cross
3. Jesus Falls for the First Time
4. Jesus Meets His Blessed Mother
5. Simon of Cyrene Helps Jesus to Carry the Cross
6. Veronica Wipes the Face of Jesus
7. Jesus Falls a Second Time
8. Jesus Consoles the Women of Jerusalem
9. Jesus Falls the Third Time
10. Jesus Is Stripped of His Garments
11. Jesus Is Nailed to the Cross
12. Jesus Dies on the Cross
13. Jesus Is Laid in the Arms of His Blessed Mother
14. Jesus Is Laid in the Tomb

Of Pope St. John Paul II

This version of the Stations of the Cross was celebrated by Pope St. John Paul II on Good Friday, 1991.

1. Jesus in the Garden of Gethsemane   (Mt 25:36–41)
2. Jesus, Betrayed by Judas, is Arrested   (Mk 14:43–46)
3. Jesus Is Condemned by the Sanhedrin   (Lk 22:66–71)
4. Jesus Is Denied by Peter   (Mt 26:69–75)
5. Jesus Is Judged by Pilate   (Mk 15:1–5, 15)
6. Jesus Is Scourged and Crowned with Thorns   (Jn 19:1–3)
7. Jesus Bears the Cross   (Jn 19:6, 15–17)
8. Jesus Is Helped by Simon the Cyrenian to Carry the Cross   (Mk 15:21)
9. Jesus Meets the Women of Jerusalem   (Lk 23:27–31)
10. Jesus Is Crucified   (Lk 23:33–34)
11. Jesus Promises His Kingdom to the Good Thief   (Lk 23:39–43)
12. Jesus Speaks to His Mother and the Disciple   (Jn 19:25–27)
13. Jesus Dies on the Cross   (Lk 23:44–46)
14. Jesus Is Placed in the Tomb   (Mt 27:57–60)

An Overview of the Sacraments

Sacrament	Matter	Form	Minister(s)	Instituted by Christ
Baptism	water	"I baptize you in the name of the Father, and of the Son, and of the Holy Spirit."	bishop, priest, or deacon; in the case of emergency, anyone may baptize, even a non-baptized person, if the intention is to do what the Church does when she baptizes	Mt 28:19–20
Confirmation	holy chrism	"Be sealed with the gift of the Holy Spirit."	a bishop is the ordinary minister of Confirmation, although a bishop may grant the faculty to a priest	Lk 24:49 Acts 2:1–4
Eucharist	wheat bread, grape wine	"…this is my Body…this is my Blood…"	bishop or priest	Mt 26:26–29 Mk 14:22–25 Lk 22:19–20 Jn 6:35–36
Penance and Reconciliation	oral confession of sins	"…I absolve you from your sins in the Name of the Father, and of the Son, and of the Holy Spirit."	bishop or priest	Mt 16:19 Mt 18:18 Jn 20:22–23
Anointing of the Sick	oil of the sick	"Through this holy anointing, may the Lord in his love and mercy help you with the grace of the Holy Spirit. May the Lord who frees you from sin, save you and raise you up."	bishop or priest	Mk 6:13 Jas 5:14–15
Holy Orders	laying on of hands	the sacramental form is the consecratory prayer that is different for the ordination of deacon, priest, or bishop	bishop	Lk 22:19 Acts 6:6
Matrimony	the couple themselves	the vows as exchanged by the couple	the couple themselves	Mk 10:7–9 Jn 2:1–11